"We're family."

A Day in the Park

Graceful Dancer

Thank you!

Pat-a-pat-a-pat

Nighty-night!

Time to Snooze

"Hello, neigh-bor!"

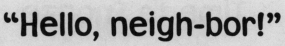

"Well, howdy!"

"It's spring!"

Hat Trick

Best Friends

Fire Fighter

"What's out here?"

The Early Bird

Collecting the Eggs

Swishy Fishy

"What a great day!"

A-OK!

Up into Space

What a view!

Under the Sea

Tennis Fun

"Good morning!"

Astro-Cat

Bubble Bath

"I see you!"

Zappy Man!

Zippy the Turtle

"Who's up there?"

Zipping Along

Peek-a-boo!

Buzzy Bee

Green means GO!

Snow Plow

Puppy Play

Balloon Buddy

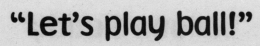

"Let's play ball!"

"Count me in!"

Helpful Crane

Trusty Truck

"Did I hear 'treat'?"

"Ice creammmm!"

A Nifty Nightcap

Happy Helicopter

Gentle Dragon

Purrr-fect Pet

Tom the Tractor

"Hello!"

World of Fun!

Tiger Time

Circus Star

Ready to Roar!

"Hello, up there."

Cuddly Pal

Let's play!

Let's play again!

Baby Giraffe

Baby Chimpanzee

Adventure Ahead

Nurse Tabby

Fun at the Pond

Catching Fireflies

Hockey Player

Just popping up to say, "Hello!"

 Pail Puppy

"Do you want to take a spin?"

In the Garden

A Lovely Day

Ice is nice!

Cruising is fun!

Snack Time

Dino Pal

7
+ 4
——
11

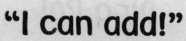
"I can add!"

"Hoops, anyone?"

Sailing the Sea

"Aye, aye, Captain."

Cute Caterpillar

Beautiful Butterfly

Dinos of the Deep

Dinos on the Land

Cuddly Giraffe

Big, Soft Elephant

Daydreaming

Treats to Share

"Get on the bus!"

"Faster, faster!"

 Crayola

Swan Lake

Summer Fun

Friendly Mouse

Cuddly Bunny

On the Farm

In the Jungle

Rough and Tough

Neat and Sweet

"Juice—coming up!"